CLASSIC LANDFORMS OF THE

LAKE
DISTRICT

CLASSIC LANDFORMS OF THE

LAKE DISTRICT

JOHN BOARDMAN
Keble College, Oxford

Series editors
Rodney Castleden and Christopher Green

Published by the Geographical Association
in conjunction with the
British Geomorphological Research Group

Geographical
Association

THE BRITISH GEOMORPHOLOGICAL RESEARCH GROUP

PREFACE

Geomorphologists study landforms and the processes that create and modify them. The results of their work, published as they invariably are in specialist journals, usually remain inaccessible to the general public. We would like to put that right. Scattered across the landscapes of England and Wales there are many beautiful and striking landforms that delight the eye of the general public and are also visited by educational parties from schools, colleges and universities. Our aim in producing this series of guides is to make modern explanations of these classic landforms available to all, in a style and format that will be easy to use in the field. We hope that an informed understanding of the origins of the features will help the visitor to enjoy the landscape all the more.

This guide to the Lakes is a project very close to our hearts, not least because it is one that we worked on for several years, but also because it exemplifies the purpose of the series. Although teachers and students look to Cumbria for classic evidence of glaciation, the latest findings, which are included here, may surprise many readers. The area has been neglected by geomorphologists and many assumptions – for instance about the origin of the radial drainage pattern, the origin of the valleys, the severity of the Devensian glaciation and rates of glacial erosion – may be wrong. We hope to provide a refreshing new perspective on a little-understood region.

The relevant maps for the area covered in this booklet are the Ordnance Survey Landranger 1:50 000 series, numbers 89 and 90; please refer to the current Ordnance Survey Index for 1:25 000 availability. The addition of 1:50 000 map extracts are included by kind permission of the Education Team, Ordnance Survey.

Rodney Castleden *Roedean School, Brighton*
Christopher Green *Royal Holloway and Bedford New College, London*

© the Geographical Association, 1988, 1996
As a benefit of membership, the Association allows members
to reproduce material for their own internal school/departmental use,
provided that the copyright is held by the GA. This waiver does not apply to
Ordnance Survey mapping, questions about which should be referred to the
Ordnance Survey.
ISBN 1 899085 25 4
This edition first published 1996, reprinted 2002.
Published by the Geographical Association, 160 Solly Street, Sheffield S1 4BF
Website: www.geography.org.uk   E-mail: ga@geography.org.uk
The views expressed in this publication are those of the author and do not
necessarily represent those of the Geographical Association.
The Geographical Association is a registered charity no. 313129
Cover photograph: Sourmilk Gill, Seathwaite *Photo:* Richard Watson
Frontispiece: Wast Water screes with Great Gable beyond *Photo:* John Boardman

CONTENTS

Introduction   *6*

Geology and Scenery   *9*

Blea Water Corrie   *13*

Wasdale   *19*

The Keswick area   *27*

Mosedale Beck valley   *39*

Patterned ground on Grasmoor   *44*

Corries of the northern Lake District   *47*

Glossary   *50*

Bibliography   *51*

Help and advice

Leaders of school parties to the Lake District requiring further help and advice on fieldwork in the area are recommended to get in touch with the Lake District National Park/Education Service, National Park Visitor Centre, Brockhole, Windermere, Cumbria LA23 1LJ (Tel. 01539 446601).

Acknowledgements

The author would like to thank Dr Ian Evans of Durham University for material that forms part of the section on corries of the northern Lake District.

The Geographical Association would like to thank the following organisations for permission to reproduce material in this publication:

Ministry of Defence (Crown Copyright Reserved) for the image of Blea Water Corrie

The Royal Society of Edinburgh for Figure 5

Geografiska Annaler for Figure 16

Mapping reproduced from Ordnance Survey 1:50 000 Landranger mapping with the permission of The Controller of Her Majesty's Stationery Office © Crown Copyright 82324M 09/96.

Copy Editing: Rose Pipes   *Illustrations:* Paul Coles

Series design concept: Quarto Design, Huddersfield

Design and typesetting: Arkima Ltd, Leeds

Printed and bound in China through Colorcraft Limited, Hong Kong

INTRODUCTION

This guide is concerned with specific sites where well developed landforms occur and where studies have been carried out. These 'classic landforms' are not representative of the Lake District landscape as a whole which is generally both more complex and less well understood. A myth has developed that the geomorphology of the Lake District has been fully understood and explained. On the contrary, although the region has been widely depicted in textbooks and referred to as possessing classic features of glaciation, much of the work is outdated and superficial. It is not a simple matter to rewrite the geomorphology of a neglected area; however, a brief overview of themes which may be suitable for teaching or research projects is given below.

The impact of glaciation

It is important not to over-rely on alpine models of valley glaciation. The Lake District has been repeatedly affected by ice-sheet glaciation, and troughs such as that of Wasdale are probably the result of such conditions (see Figure 1). There are few of the classic features of alpine glaciation, such as hanging valleys or terminal and lateral moraines.

The impact of a restricted glaciation, the Loch Lomond Advance, is particularly clear in many corries and valley heads in the central Lake District. The evidence is in the form of depositional landforms; its erosional impact was slight.

The erosional impact of multiple glaciations is very difficult to assess because the form of the pre-glacial landscape is unknown. The over-deepening of basins suggests some erosional impact but firm evidence in support of the cutting of the troughs is lacking. A radial, pre-glacial drainage pattern which was accentuated by glacial processes seems most likely but in this matter, as in others, there are minimalist and maximalist viewpoints! The impact of the last major glaciation, that which occurred during the **Dimlington Stadial**, seems to have been overrated. The survival of pre-Devensian **till** along a routeway for ice movement argues for little erosion during the glaciation; this view is in contrast to those expressed in authoritative texts, for example, those by Professors King and Moseley.

The existence of over 50 well-developed corries is unequivocal evidence that parts of the landscape were affected by glacial erosion for long periods of time during the Quaternary.

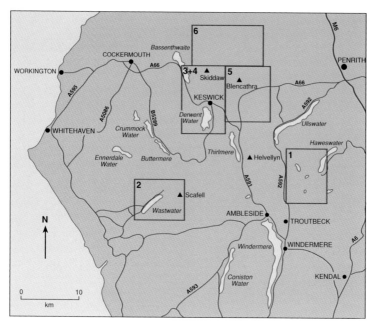

Figure 1: Areas of the Lake District covered in this book

Almost all of the depositional evidence for glaciation relates to the Devensian and reflects both phases of active subglacial sedimentation and later stagnation. These events are reasonably well understood not least because they fall within the time scale of radio-carbon dating.

The impact of periglaciation

There have been many more studies of the glacial impact on the landscape of the Lake District than of the periglacial. Consequently there is a dearth of information about the latter: for example, the alluvial fans of the area are almost certainly periglacial in origin and are likely to contain clues as to the environmental history of their basins, but the research remains to be done.

The primary periglacial feature of the Lake District is scree, but scree deposits are frequently concealed by vegetation. Cuttings in forestry roads such as those in Dodd Wood and Thornthwaite Forest near Keswick indicate the true extent and variability of the scree.

The present interglacial

For the last 10 000 years the Lake District landscape has been relatively stable in terms of geomorphological change. No classic landforms have developed and existing ones have altered little. This is because of the slow rate of operation of geomorphological processes today compared with those under glacial and periglacial conditions. With the landscape vegetated, at least to around 650m, runoff and sediment transport on slopes have been greatly reduced. And this seems to be true even in high-gradient catchments.

The major landscape change during the Flandrian has been deforestation. Soil profiles, drainage and runoff have been affected but there is virtually no information from the Lake District which allows us to contrast the forested landscape of the earlier part of the interglacial with the more recent deforested landscape.

The landforms of the Lake District are typical of those of the western and northern uplands of Britain both in a spatial and temporal sense. They are characteristic landforms of the Quaternary period which, in these latitudes, has been dominated by cold-climate processes.

GEOLOGY AND SCENERY

The bedrock geology of the Lake District is illustrated in Figure 2. The oldest rocks, confined largely to the north, are those of the Skiddaw Group. These are thinly cleaved mudstones with occasional more massive sandstone beds and are popularly known as Skiddaw Slate. In the area between the summit of Skiddaw (NY 260291) and Mungrisdale (NY 362304) the slate has been thermally metamorphosed by the intrusion of the Skiddaw Granite: this may explain the resistance to erosion of this mountain mass. The scenery developed on this relatively homogenous group of rocks tends to be dominated by smooth slopes unbroken by rock outcrops. Overlying the Skiddaw Slate is the Eycott Group of extrusive igneous rocks which are mainly **basalts** and **andesites.**

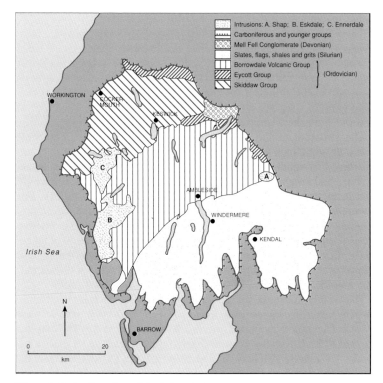

Figure 2: Bedrock geology of the Lake District

The central Lake District is dominated by the Borrowdale Volcanic Group which is made up of over 5000m of lavas and **pyroclastic rocks**, principally ashfall tuffs, or volcanic ashes. The latter, having been metamorphosed, are often fine grained and thinly cleaved; they were deposited in a marine environment and frequently display spectacular sedimentary features – when cut and polished they can be used for ornamental stonework to make decorative objects. Green-slate quarries and workings can be seen at Coniston, Langdale, Kirkstone and Honister. The variety of rock types within the Borrowdale Volcanic Group gives rise to the rugged stepped topography of the central Lake District. Resistant beds stand out as steep cliffs.

Both Skiddaw Group and Borrowdale Volcanic Group rocks are of Ordovician age; that is, they were formed between about 500 and 440 million years ago. They are the result of deep water sedimentation being succeeded by vulcanism along the line of collision between continental plates approaching one another from north-west and south-east.

The southern Lake District is underlain by sedimentary rocks of Silurian age (440 to 410 million years old). These rocks are shales, flags, grits and slates – less resistant than the Borrowdale Group and more varied than the Skiddaw Group. The result is topography on a smaller scale than that of the central Lake District: the south lacks the relief to show the full effects of highland glaciation.

Three important granitic intrusions influence the scenery of the Lake District: those of Shap, Ennerdale and Eskdale. Outcrops of these granites appear to represent the exposed parts of a large **batholith** which underlies the northern Lake District. The Skiddaw Granite is also part of the batholith but is only exposed at three small localities. The granites may not all be of the same age but were emplaced at various times between the Ordovician and Devonian periods.

The structure of the central Lake District is complex. East-west trending anticlines and synclines, such as the Scafell Syncline, are disrupted by south-west to north-east trending faults. Faulting seems to have had a significant influence on later erosional events, especially the location of some of the lakes and the direction of valleys. For example, a prominent fault runs from Coniston through Grasmere, Dunmail Raise, Thirlmere and St John's in the Vale. The relative resistance of rocks seems also to have influenced the location of lakes: only three of the major lakes – Thirlmere, Wast Water and Haweswater – are developed on the Borrowdale Volcanic Group outcrop; the majority are in areas of softer rocks to the north and south.

The widely discussed radial drainage pattern of the Lake District is usually described as resulting from the superimposition onto old hard rocks of a pattern developed on a dome of younger rocks. The doming is said to be a Tertiary event (65 to 2 million years ago); the young rocks have been stripped off the central Lake District but remain around the periphery. What is controversial is the extent to which the radial pattern has been modified by glaciation.

In many parts of the Lake District the bedrock geology is concealed beneath unconsolidated deposits of the Quaternary age, that is the last 2 million years, a period characterised by global climatic change. In Britain the climate oscillated from warm (interglacial) to cold (glacial) conditions.

In the Lake District, only sediments deposited in the most recent part of the Quaternary have been identified. Figure 3 therefore covers the last 130 000 years and gives the names which are used in Britain to distinguish sub-divisions of this time period. Of particular importance are the glacial events that occurred in the Lake District during the **Dimlington** and **Loch Lomond Stadials**. During the former, northern Britain was covered by a very thick ice sheet, perhaps 700m above the

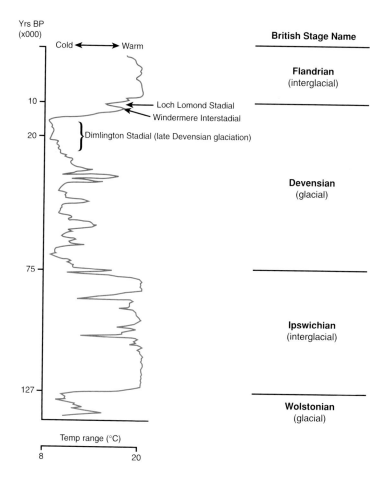

Figure 3: Late Quaternary climatic change in Britain
Temperature range is July average for English Midlands

highest of the Lake District mountains. The growth and decay of this sheet took over 10 000 years; by contrast, the Loch Lomond Stadial, the most recent cold period to affect Britain, lasted for less than 1000 years. Its scale and extent is especially clear in the Lake District, where it caused the formation of glaciers in some of the corries and valleys. Because the extent and style of glaciation are different in the two cold periods it is possible to distinguish the resulting depositional landforms and sediments. As we shall see, erosional landforms are more difficult to deal with.

The geology of the Lake District is described in detail in many books. For a modern synthesis, that edited by Professor F. Moseley is recommended (see Bibliography). Many non-specialists have been introduced to the subject by the books of E.H. Shackleton: his descriptions of Lake District localities of geological interest are invaluable.

BLEA WATER CORRIE

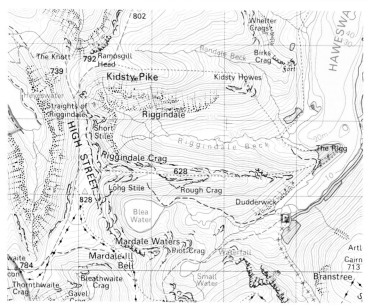

© *Crown Copyright*

In the late nineteenth century, argument about the possible glacial origin of corries centred on their form: were they true rock basins or merely valley heads with moraines around them? Modern surveys have shown the former to be frequently the case and a glacial origin was accepted around 1900.

Blea Water Corrie, or cirque, is of classic form: it is large and deep and in the context of the Lake District it is possible to suggest why this site was especially favourable for corrie development. It is in the lee of a mountain mass, High Street, whose wide summit area acted as a snow gathering ground; snow blown from here accumulated in valley heads and incipient corries (Figure 4). Westerly and southerly winds would have led to the build-up of snow in Blea Water Corrie. The corrie faces east-north-east and, so accumulating snow received some protection from the sun. As the corrie deepened both the snow-blow and solar effects would increase.

Blea Water (Photo 1), occupies a rock-cut basin – the greatest water depth is 63m and the deepest point is 96m below the top of the central part of the moraine-covered lip. Air photographs suggest that the impression gained on the ground – of a massive moraine ridge – is

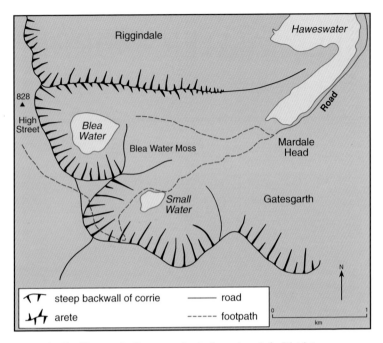

Figure 4: Blea Water and adjacent corries in the eastern Lake District

misleading and that the lip is quite thinly covered by glacial sediments. The corrie is therefore a substantially over-deepened basin and Lewis' explanation, based on comparisons with modern Norwegian glaciers, is that deepening was achieved by the rotational flow of a small corrie glacier:

'The annually renewed load of firn and ice near the headwall transmits its pressure so as to push the ice near its snout uphill. This ice can be lifted all the easier owing to the annual losses by summer ablation. Rotational movement would lead to relatively high velocity near the bed, especially along the critical zone where the ice rises towards the crest of the lip. The arcuate nature of the long profiles through Blea Water Corrie would also seem to point to the action of some form of rotating ice mass' (Lewis, 1960, p. 98).

The theory that an ice mass with a tendency to rotational flow occupied the corrie was of great importance in advancing our understanding of corrie formation. In practice, there must have been many occasions when larger or smaller ice masses occupied the corrie. The map by Dr J.B. Sissons (Figure 5) clearly shows the relationship of ice and landscape during the Loch Lomond Stadial and depicts the maximum ice extent, which occurred around 10 500 **BP**. At this time ice masses from the adjacent corries of Blea Water and Small Water (glacier 57 on Figure 5) were confluent and almost reached Mardale Head, the present southern end of Haweswater.

Photo 1: Blea Water Corrie
Crown Copyright reserved

Sissons' reconstruction of the maximum extent of ice is based on the distribution of landforms indicating the most recent glacial limits. Landforms relating to the decay of the Late Devensian ice sheet are not shown: these are generally more degraded than the more recent limits and are sometimes in locations such as cols which do not relate to the phase of corrie glaciation. The distinctiveness of the evidence for what is now known as the Loch Lomond Advance was recognised by Marr in his *Geology of the Lake District:*

'Even if the large valley-glaciers were merely a stage in the waning of the ice-sheet, it is possible that the latest corrie-glaciers were the products of a distinct and very recent glaciation. Their relics are so fresh that we can hardly suppose a long period of time to have elapsed since their occupation of the combes' (Marr, 1916, p. 196).

It is important to remember that writers such as Marr had no means of dating glacial events. Their deductions about landscape evolution were based entirely on landform evidence. The development of radio-carbon dating in 1950, and other dating techniques thereafter, gave geomorphologists a valuable tool, though one which leaves many problems still unresolved.

Figure 5, based on geomorphological mapping by Dr J. B. Sissons, is a useful accompaniment to a field excursion in the area. The glaciers may be accurately transferred to a 1:25 000 Ordnance Survey map. The path from Mardale Head to Blea Water Corrie skirts an area

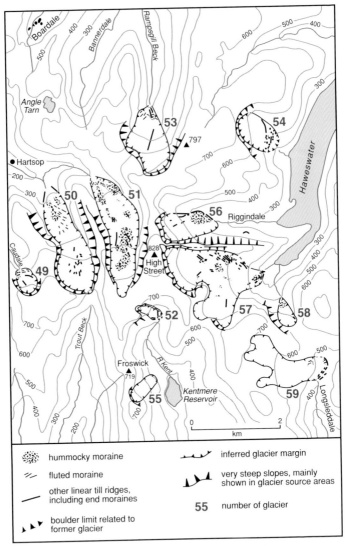

Figure 5: Loch Lomond Stadial glaciers in the eastern Lake District After Sissons, 1980

of hummocky moraine near the snout of the former glacier (NY 465105). Much of the material in the mounds travelled as en-glacial and supra-glacial debris and was dumped among wasting ice as the climate improved. On steeper slopes the ice edge retreated and left a fine series of lateral moraines, perhaps representing annual still-stands during retreat (Photo 2).

One curious feature of Sissons' reconstruction is that the moraine plastered onto the lip of Blea Water Corrie is not shown. The moraine is some distance from the glacier limits and it seems probable that the ice retreated into the corrie and then constructed a moraine – either

Photo 2: Lateral moraines formed along the margin of the Loch Lomond Stadial glacier at Blea Water Corrie (NY 457110) Photo: John Boardman

from newly eroded material or by the reworking of pre-existing till. Alternatively, the moraine is pre-Loch Lomond Stadial in age and was overridden and smoothed by stadial ice as it moved out of the corrie.

Below the rock step which forms the lip of Blea Water Corrie is a marshy, infilled basin, Blea Water Moss (Figure 4). Professor Pennington has shown, using plant pollen evidence, that Blea Water Moss became ice-free during the Loch Lomond Stadial prior to the Small Water Corrie which in turn was deglaciated before the Blea Water Corrie. The latter appears to have retained its ice mass longer than any other site in the Lake District, thereby emphasising its favoured location. Final melting only occurred after the beginning of the major climatic warming at the opening of the Flandrian, about 10 000 BP.

Further consideration of Figure 5 shows that during the Loch Lomond Stadial not all valley-head sites in the eastern Lake District were occupied by ice. Glaciers were restricted to the north-and east-facing higher valleys and corries such as Riggindale (glacier 56 on Figure 5) and Gatesgarth (glacier 58). To a large extent, previously glacierised sites were re-occupied – the process was self perpetuating. Valleys such as Bannerdale, although north-facing, lacked the steep, glaciated valley walls and thus could not offer sufficient shade for the development of glacier ice.

For a general view of the effects of glaciation no better vantage point is to be found than the summit plateau of High Street. Particularly impressive is the Hayeswater valley (glacier 51) with its superb moraines and its clearly defined ice limit (see Photo 3).

Photo 3: Hayeswater from High Street looking north
The lake is surrounded by Loch Lomond Stadial moraine, interrupted on the eastern side by a large alluvial fan. The Hayeswater glacier is numbered 51 on Figure 5
Photo: John Boardman

It is worth emphasising that corrie development must have required repeated glacial phases not unlike that of the Loch Lomond Stadial. Regional glaciation, when the whole landscape was submerged by ice, can have played little part in corrie formation. Instead, we must postulate episodes of limited snow availability and temperature conditions which sustained small glaciers. This serves to underline the importance of the Loch Lomond Advance. It provides the only model we have for a phase of restricted glaciation – restricted that is to the development of small ice caps and corrie and valley glaciers in western Britain. Such phases may have preceded and followed periods of more extensive glaciation but they may also have occurred during those long periods of time for which we have evidence of considerable cold but apparently no major ice sheets in northern Britain (Figure 3).

Access and safety

There is no coach access to Mardale Head although parking is available for smaller vehicles. Well marked footpaths may be followed to either Blea Water or Small Water. The ascent of High Street (see Figure 4) should not be attempted in poor weather conditions.

WASDALE

© Crown Copyright

Evidence of glacial erosion is particularly well displayed in Wasdale, though most visitors to the area will remember it for the screes – a postglacial depositional landform.

The form of the valley is, in cross section, that of a typical glaciated trough, steep sided and relatively flat bottomed; the latter aspect being partly a function of glacial deposition and post-glacial alluviation. In long profile Wast Water occupies a glacially over-deepened basin. The surface of the lake is at 61m OD and its maximum depth is 76m, that is, 15m below sea level. It is the deepest lake in the Lake District and one of the few that can be shown conclusively to occupy a rock-cut basin. The over-deepening terminates where ice, having been confined within the trough, spread out onto the lowland around Nether Wasdale (Figure 6).

The popular idea of valleys such as Wasdale being cut by valley glaciers may be incorrect. An alternative model envisages an ice sheet covering the Lake District within which fast moving streams of ice are located in pre-existing valleys. Little erosion takes place on the interfluves where thin, slowly-moving ice is frozen to the bedrock. The thicker ice in the valleys slides rapidly over the rock surface aided by a thin film of meltwater. Erosion is therefore concentrated in the valleys, enhancing the contrast between interfluve and valley. True

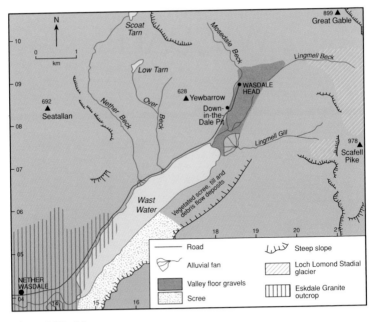

Figure 6: Wasdale area

True valley glaciers would have occupied the valleys at the beginning and end of cold periods and corries would have filled with ice at the same time. Accordant summit heights in the Lake District, which may represent the remains of pre-glacial erosion surfaces, can be used in support of the idea that the landscape is essentially one of 'selective linear erosion', a model favoured by Professor D.E. Sugden for the uplands of north-eastern Scotland.

If the exact mode of glacial erosion is open to debate, so too is the amount. Is the full depth of Wasdale the result of glacial processes or have they merely *contributed* to its present size? The evidence is equivocal and a number of alternatives may be suggested. A minimum figure is the 15m of over-deepening of the lake basin, whereas at least 40m is suggested by the fact that the Mosedale valley 'hangs' above Wasdale (Figure 6). A maximum amount of around 600m is obtained from the difference between the summit heights to the north and south of the lake and the valley bottom. Current rates of downcutting by valley glaciers are of the order of 1mm per year or 1m per 1000 years: 600m erosion might therefore be accomplished in 600 000 years – a figure within the bounds of possibility in relation to the known duration of Quaternary cold periods. Fast-moving ice streams within ice sheets are probably much more effective agents of erosion than valley glaciers. However, there are problems with many aspects of these arguments: hanging valley relationships need not be glacial in origin, and it is likely that valley systems existed in the Lake District before the onset of glaciation. It is therefore impossible to reconstruct the pre-glacial landscape with any confidence.

Examination of the present slopes of Wasdale shows that if glaciers were to return to the valley they would have little difficulty in removing large quantities of debris. This suggests that glaciers transport material prepared by weathering processes during periglacial and temperate periods and that their effectiveness as agents of landscape change may have little to do with their ability to erode solid rock.

As well as the over-deepening of the valley, there is other evidence for glaciation:

1. Between Wasdale Hall and Water Crag, on the south-west shores of the lake, is an area of irregular hummocks in solid rock; such landscapes, known as knock and lochan topography, are typical of heavily glaciated areas in well-jointed rocks – in this case the Eskdale Granite (Figure 2). Many of the rock hummocks, or roches moutonnées, are smoothed by abrasion on the up-glacier side and 'plucked' on the down-glacier side. The efficacy of plucking is now in doubt and alternative mechanisms have been proposed. Block removal may be achieved by freeze-thaw action in temporary cavities beneath the ice or by rock fracture due to boulder impact. Striations are rare because of postglacial weathering of the abraded surfaces.

2. Between Nether Wasdale and Easthwaite (NY 137034) the solid geology is largely obscured by sand and gravel and till hummocks deposited by melting stagnant ice.

3. Around Wast Water itself, glacial sediments are usually masked by slope deposits but by the path south of Wasdale Head Hall Farm (NY 180068) there are good exposures of grey sandy till containing sub-rounded stones. A brownish soil is developed in the upper 1m.

Erosional landforms are notoriously difficult to date. However, it is reasonable to assume that glacial sediments, the till and sands and gravels, are Devensian in age: certainly those in exposed locations would not have survived from a previous glaciation. Erosional landforms were modified by the last glaciation but the scale of this modification is unknown. So is the length of time that the Lakeland valleys were occupied by Devensian ice: it could have been anything from 20 000 to 70 000 years. Professor Boulton has suggested that the growth of the last British ice sheet in the Late Devensian may have taken 15 000 years, from about 33 000 to 18 000 BP, but valley and corrie glaciers may have existed in the Lake District for thousands of years before that.

The last ice melted in the major valleys about 15 000 years ago. Since then the climate, apart from one brief spell, has been temperate and soil formation, fluvial activity and scree formation have been the principal processes.

The screes of Wasdale (Photo 4) are frequently referred to but have not been subject to detailed study. They are composed of a series of

21

coalescing **talus** cones emanating from gullies along 2.6km of a north-west facing slope. Typically, free face and gullies lie between 250 and 500m OD; below this the screes reach down to, and below, the lake surface at 61m OD. The screes are composed of sub-angular and angular fragments of andesite varying in size from 2.5 to 60cm. On measured profiles slope angles of between 30° and 36° have been recorded. They are not straight slopes; variations are due to the angle of rest of differently sized material and the occurrence of talus slides.

Photo 4: Wast Water screes   *Photo: John Boardman*

It is generally assumed that the major process promoting rockfall to the scree surface is frost wedging. The frequency of rockfall at the present time is unknown. Even a brief inspection of the screes shows that parts are vegetated and stable while others are still active and movements of the finer areas are easily triggered by human or animal encroachment. Despite this it is clear that large areas are in what Professor J.T. Andrews calls 'a retarded state of development'. He postulates a time in the past when the screes were more actively forming – perhaps the **Little Ice Age** of the sixteenth and seventeenth centuries. There is also the possibility that the screes are largely Late Glacial, formed when localised glaciation returned to the area during the Loch Lomond Stadial. A more radical suggestion is that they have little to do with frost action and are the result of the removal of loading by ice during deglaciation. This would allow expansion of the rocks, joint formation (pressure release joints) and, inevitably, rockfall. It is difficult to assess such an idea in the absence of monitoring of both rockfalls and climate.

The relative stability of various parts of the screes is worthy of examination. Vegetation criteria have been proposed by W. Leach for Lake District scree stability: lichens and bryophytes ➔ parsley fern (*Cryptogramma cripsa*) ➔ other ferns with grasses ➔ heather (*Calluna*) ➔ trees. Soil development and therefore colonisation by vegetation is more rapid on material of small particle size. The origin of the fine material among the larger blocks is a puzzle: wind transport, rockfall or *in situ* weathering are possibilities. Work in the early 1980s on screes in New Zealand has shown that subtle colour changes occur as rock particles undergo weathering and that these can be used as a dating tool. This technique could be tested on the Wasdale screes.

At the northern end, valley-side slopes on both sides of Wast Water have continuous vegetation cover, but small exposures show that they are frequently underlain by angular rock particles in a finer matrix. An excellent example is seen in the roadside pit at Down-in-the-Dale Bridge (NY 183082). Poorly sorted, angular sandy gravel contains occasional sub-angular glaciated particles. Bedding is also visible in the north face of the pit. Measurement of the dip and orientation of the long axes of gravel particles suggests that they form part of a slope deposit which accumulated by sliding and rolling after rockfall from the now inactive free faces (Figure 7). Washing of the upper layers also occurred and from a distance the surface form can be seen to be that of a fan. The stream that contributed to its formation now flows to the south of the exposure.

The sandy gravel in this pit is an extremely cohesive deposit and many particles have silt and clay cappings on their upper surfaces. Such indurated or tough, dense horizons, with evidence of silt and

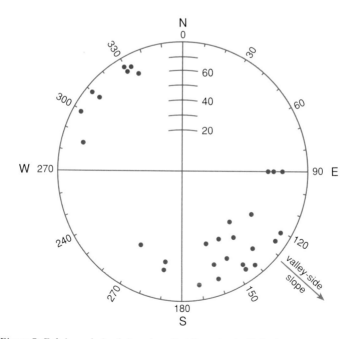

Figure 7: Fabric analysis of slope deposit at Down-in-the-Dale pit
The orientation of the long axis of each elongate particle is plotted with respect to magnetic north (0°). The dip of the long axis is indicated by the distance from the centre to the outer circle (0°). For details see Briggs, 1977, ch. 5

23

clay movement from higher in the profile, are known as fragipans and are thought to be relict features inherited from deeply frozen soils. The high bulk density of the fragipan is a result of stresses exerted by the growth of ice lenses in the soil. Fragic horizons are also seen in nearby exposures at NY 181076 and NY 160065. Their occurrence suggests that these slopes have been stable and inactive throughout the Flandrian – perhaps in contrast to the scree slopes on the opposite valley side.

Apart from the scree slopes in Wasdale, the main focus of landscape modification during the Flandrian has been in the river channel. High-gradient mountain streams are capable of gravel transport but this material is deposited on low-gradient valley floors or in bodies of still water. A series of large alluvial gravel fans, presumably extending into the lake as deltas, exist around Wast Water (Figure 6 and Photo 5).

At the head of the lake two fans form an extensive area of low ground. Their size is roughly a function of basin area and hence stream discharge (Table 1). The gradient of the fan surface appears to reflect the size of sediment available for transport. The high gradient of the Lingmell Gill fan is a necessary adjustment if the stream

Photo 5: The head of Wast Water
A gravel fan encroaches into the lake. The heavily eroded path to Scafell Pike can be seen following Lingmell Gill Photo: John Boardman

24

channel is to carry very coarse sediment in relatively low discharges. The size of sediment moved down the Lingmell Gill channel may be seen by walking up the beck from the car park (NY 181075). The present stream is reworking coarse gravels that form part of an older higher fan. In this, the wettest part of England, high-gradient streams are capable of considerable landscape modification but the major erosional impact is limited to points at which streams impinge on valley-side slopes composed of easily eroded material: former alluvial deposits, periglacial slope deposits and glacial till. In this way, materials that have been in storage, often throughout the Flandrian, are moved to lake basin or floodplain sites.

In a largely vegetated landscape, rates of supply of material to streams are limited and so, therefore, are transport rates. Table 2 is based on the sparse available data and contrasts present-day rates of transport in the Lake District with those operating under periglacial conditions in the same area.

Two further points relating to fan development may be noted. First, parts of the catchments of these streams probably receive as much as 4000mm of precipitation per year. Second, Dr J.B. Sissons has shown that glaciers occupied corries in both these catchments during the Loch Lomond Stadial (Figure 6). Alluvial fan development would certainly have been active during this period of glacial and periglacial conditions.

Table 1: Basin and fan characteristics at the head of Wast Water

Basin	Basin area (km2)	Fan area (km2)	Channel gradient	Sediment size (cm)[a]	Percentage glacierised[b]
Mosedale Beck/ Lingmell Beck	17.6	1.053	0.005	17	17.8
Lingmell Gill	2.9	0.193	0.05	32	10.3

Notes: a. Mean size of largest 30 boulders in channel on fan; sampling locations NY 181075 and NY 183074; b. During Loch Lomond Stadial: glacier areas from Sissons, 1980.

Table 2: Sediment transport by high-gradient streams in the Lake District

	Catchment area (km2)	Mean channel gradient	Bedload yield (t/km2/yr)
		present day[a]	
Beckthorn	0.5	0.40	77
Coledale	6.0	0.11	50
Lanthwaite	4.0	0.14	29
		Loch Lomond Stadial[b]	
Sandbeds	0.3	0.51	918

Notes: a. Data from Newson and Leeks, 1985; b. Data from Boardman, 1985

Access and safety

There is no coach access to Wasdale Head. The road is suitable for mini-buses. The features described in this section can be examined by walking from two points. Roadside parking exists in the vicinity of the road junction at NY 151054 which is a good viewpoint for the screes. The car park at the head of the lake is convenient for a study of the stream channels on the fans and as a departure point for the lakeside walk along the base of the screes. This path is clearly marked on the OS map but is not so easily followed on the ground. The result of straying from the path will be a scramble among large boulders. Care should be taken because some of these boulders are unstable. It is not necessary to venture onto the upper screes – slides can be started and this can be a dangerous area. The screes can be adequately examined from the lakeside path.

THE KESWICK AREA

Castlehead

From the top of Castlehead (NY 270227), a superb viewpoint attained with relatively little effort, the relationship of geology and scenery in the Keswick area can be clearly seen (Figure 8 and Photo 6).

The major topographic feature, the Derwent valley, is clearly seen from Castlehead; to the south of Keswick it is known as Borrowdale. The valley floor is partly occupied by two shallow lakes: Derwent Water, with a maximum depth of 22m and Bassenthwaite Lake, with a depth of 19m. The valley has the appearance of having been glaciated and glaciation has certainly had some influence on its configuration. Derwent Water probably occupies a rock basin and Bassenthwaite is dammed by glacial debris, thus changing the course of the Derwent as it leaves the lake from its pre-glacial route along the Embleton valley to a more northerly course.

Photo 6: Derwent Water from Castlehead
Looking south along the glaciated valley of Borrowdale   Photo: John Boardman

Hanging valleys are rare in the Lake District but the entry of Watendlath Beck into the main Derwent valley via Lodore Falls (NY 261187) is an excellent example. However, it serves to make the point that geological rather than glaciological factors often provide an adequate explanation of the hanging relationship. The boundary

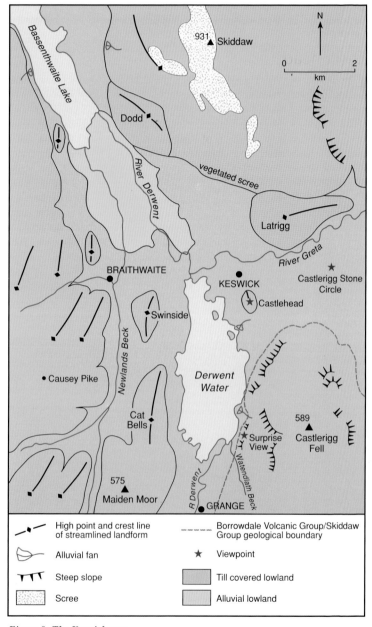

Figure 8: The Keswick area

between the Borrowdale Volcanic Group and the Skiddaw Group runs along the eastern shore of the lake, the lake basin is excavated in the softer slates, and the precipitous eastern slopes of the valley are formed of resistant Borrowdale Group rocks – hence the existence of waterfalls such as Lodore and well-known climbing cliffs such as Shepherd's Crag (NY 263184).

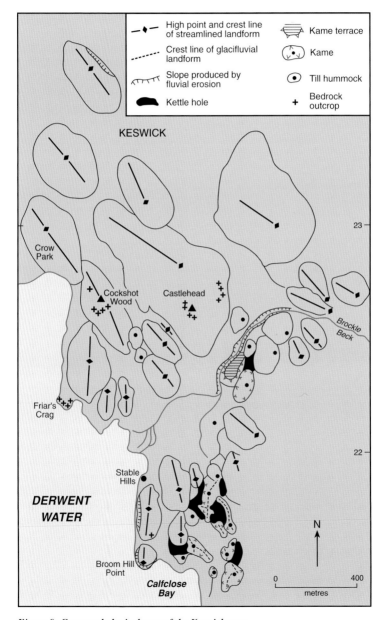

Figure 9: Geomorphological map of the Keswick area

South of Grange (NY 253175) the upper part of the Derwent valley is narrow and cut entirely in Borrowdale Group rocks. The abrupt widening of the valley at Grange is related to the presence of slates. The orientation of the lower Derwent valley may be influenced by the presence of a fault running through Skiddaw Group rocks from Braithwaite (NY 232236) to the northern end of Bassenthwaite Lake.

The topographic contrast between the scenery developed on these two major groups has often been described. The slates form rounded, smooth hill slopes due to their relatively uniform resistance to weathering and erosional processes, and also because many of the slopes are thickly covered in scree deposits beneath a cover of vegetation. The abundance of scree is due to the ease with which the thinly-cleaved slates are broken down by the freezing and thawing of water acting along the line of cleavage. In contrast, there is considerable variation in the resistance of beds within the Borrowdale Group; for example, the lavas and tuffs which give the characteristic stepped topography to hills along the eastern lake side.

It is clear that geological factors are important in explaining the landscape, but because the appearance of the landscape prior to glaciation is not known its influence is more difficult to evaluate. If we could be confident of our ability to recognise characteristic glacial forms such as troughs and hanging valleys then the difficulty would be overcome. It is likely that glaciation merely deepened and accentuated river valleys that were already established along lines of lithological and structural weakness.

Castlehead itself is formed of **dolerite:** it is the neck of a volcano which may have been responsible for the outpouring of magma which forms part of the Borrowdale Volcanic Group of rocks. Other related outcrops of dolerite occur in Cockshot Wood and Friar's Crag and can be located from Castlehead (Figure 9). The dolerite has been intruded into Skiddaw Slate and the boundary can be inspected and followed on the lake shore around the base of Friar's Crag.

Millions of years after the cooling of the dolerite, the resistant outcrops acted as the cores of drumlins. During the last glaciation, till was plastered around the outcrops and moulded by the moving ice into streamlined forms. Even on a 1:25 000 scale map the streamlining can be picked out. Castlehead itself is the largest of these streamlined forms – some prefer to call them crag and tail or rock drumlins but such terms are unhelpful since in the majority of cases we do not know what the interior of drumlins contain: in the absence of this information it is preferable to use the term 'drumlin' or 'streamlined form'.

Finally, from Castlehead can be seen the suite of drumlins which runs northwards from Calfclose Bay through the town of Keswick and onto the low-lying land to the north of the town. It includes several of the islands in Derwent Water and continues along the eastern shore of Bassenthwaite towards the Solway Plain.

The Keswick lowland

The Castlehead viewpoint allows us to see the main elements of the landscape. To appreciate individual landforms fully it is necessary to walk among them.

From the town centre of Keswick, Lake Road leads to the landing stages and Friar's Crag. It passes between two drumlins, those of Crow Park and Cockshot Wood (Figure 9). On Crow Park, the smooth streamlined form can be appreciated. The crest line, trending south-east north-west, indicates the direction of ice movement and can be seen to correspond fairly closely with those of other drumlins in the area, particularly those on which the town of Keswick is built. Looking to the north from Crow Park across the miniature golf course, the next drumlin can be seen with the line of houses along The Heads curving around its base. It is reasonable to assume that, in this area, ice movement was from the south rather than from the north since the high ground of the central Lake District is to the south. Erratics in till exposures on these drumlins confirm this assumption. However, the traditional idea that the alignment of drumlins, with their broad, high stoss ends facing up-glacier, is evidence of ice direction is incorrect the high point on drumlins may occur at either end and cannot be used as evidence of ice direction.

The path from Friar's Crag to Stable Hills and Broom Hill Point skirts several drumlins (Figure 9). Those around Stable Hills are especially well developed. Exposures in the lake-shore cliff at Broom Hill Point, where a small drumlin has been eroded, show a tough, stony till. Both slate and volcanic rock types occur in the till and the shoreline is littered with boulders that remained after the retreat of the cliff. Stones within tills which have been plastered onto the landscape generally adopt a position of least resistance in response to stress. The orientation of the long axes of stones within the till at Broom Hill Point shows a strong north-south pattern confirming the evidence of streamlined landforms that the direction of ice movement was south-north. Although this site is easily accessible and the results are rewarding, the measurements will take some time to make because of the toughness of the till due to the presence, once again, of a deep fragic horizon.

In the area to the north of Calfclose Bay the landscape is dominated by relatively large-scale landforms composed of till (Figure 9). However, there is an area of smaller scale landforms which differ in two fundamental ways: they are non-streamlined and are composed of sand and gravel. These landforms tend to be low, linear features, often curving and occasionally anastomosing. Crest lines rise and fall and enclosed or poorly drained hollows occur between the mounds or ridges. Good exposures are infrequent but rabbit holes indicate that well sorted sands and fine gravels are the principal materials. This is an area of eskers and kames representing deposition of fluvially sorted sediments in hollows and tunnels beneath and around blocks of decaying, stagnant ice. A good example of an esker occurs at NY 271219 and runs south from this point before dividing into a number of ridges.

Around Stable Hills we have evidence of two distinct phases in the development of the glacial landscape. Streamlined landforms represent deposition and moulding beneath actively flowing ice moving in a northerly direction. A later phase of ice stagnation is represented by the eskers, kames and kettle holes; in some cases these can be seen to be superimposed on the earlier streamlined forms.

Periglacial slope deposits

In the Keswick area, the characteristic smoothness of the Skiddaw Slate hills is a function of extensive superficial deposits covering the slate bedrock; if they were stripped off a very irregular landscape would be revealed. These deposits are vegetated to altitudes which vary between 500m and 900m; active or semi-active scree occurs above this altitude and occasionally at lower altitudes below steep rock faces (Figure 8).

The various components of the superficial cover can be seen along, or close to, the A592 from Keswick northwards along the eastern shore of Bassenthwaite Lake. At several localities roadside exposures show glacial till overlying bedrock, for example in the small parking area at NY 234292. The till, of Dimlington Stadial age, is frequently seen to be overlain by the younger scree deposits (Figure 3).

Along the many forestry roads on Dodd (NY 245273) typical scree deposits are seen. They are composed of angular particles of slate of many sizes. The susceptibility of slate to frost means that it breaks down into long flat particles which readily slide after their detachment from rock outcrops or from larger blocks. In sliding, they adopt a characteristic pattern, or fabric, with the long axes of the particles pointing in the direction of the movement, usually that of the

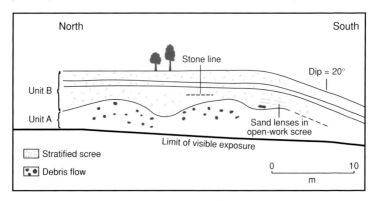

Figure 10: Periglacial slope deposits at Throstle Shaw
Sand lenses are lense-shaped beds of sand, the open-work scree in which they lie has no finer matrix

maximum slope. Where material has moved a short distance from its origin the scree is poorly sorted being made up of gravel-size particles (>2mm) with small amounts of sand, silt and clay.

Exposures at low altitudes are apt to be temporary; the slopes degrade and become vegetated. At the present time an excellent exposure exists at Throstle Shaw (NY 237272) where the construction of a forestry road has provided a vertical exposure in several metres of superficial deposits. The main section of interest is shown in Figure 10. Several metres to the north of this section Skiddaw Slate outcrops beneath the superficial cover.

At the base of the section is a poorly sorted deposit, unit A, which contains angular blocky slate and some better rounded erratic material. Particle size characteristics and the low number of striated glacial particles suggests that this is not a till. The orientation of particles indicates downslope movement towards the west in contrast to glacial material in the area which has been transported from the south. The unit is interpreted as debris flow resulting from downslope mass movement of frost shattered material which incorporated small quantities of glacial and fluvial debris. Particle size data is particularly useful in distinguishing this type of sediment from a glacial till, since the latter usually contains considerable amounts of silt and clay produced by glacial abrasion (Figure 11).

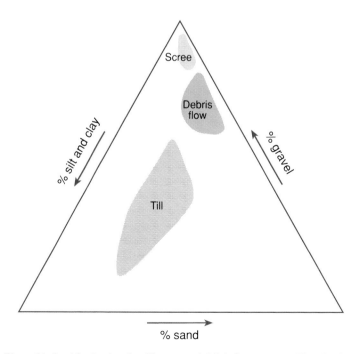

Figure 11: Particle-size data for till, scree and debris flow (unit A at Throstle Shaw) *deposits from the Keswick area*

Unit B, above the debris flow deposit, is composed of angular slate fragments. It is relatively well sorted and in places distinct beds can be identified. The angularity of the fragments suggests short-distance transport of frost-shattered debris or a continuation of shattering during sliding. Its well sorted character is atypical of scree which is the result simply of rockfall and sliding. This type of deposit is known as 'stratified scree' and is the result of sorting and transport by water after detachment of blocks from free faces. It is most likely that the water was provided by seasonal melting of snow and that flow occurred over frozen ground. In the Canadian Arctic modern analogues for these processes have been studied where **permafrost** close to the surface prevents infiltration and allows runoff across the scree.

Scree deposits such as those described in this section are no longer accumulating at low altitude sites in the Keswick area. Frost shattering and active slope processes of this nature would require a periglacial environment and a landscape with very little vegetation. Since the major glacial event during the Dimlington Stadial, periglacial climates have affected these slopes in the period immediately following deglaciation and during the Loch Lomond Stadial (Figure 3).

The Mungrisdale area

The main road from Penrith to Keswick reaches its highest point near Troutbeck Station (NY 390270) and then descends into the Glenderamackin valley (Figure 12). The truncated spurs of Blencathra (Photo 7) are clearly seen from Troutbeck. During the last glaciation, and probably many previous glacial episodes, ice moved

Photo 7: Truncated spurs of Blencathra seen from the south across the Vale of Threlkeld
Photo: John Boardman

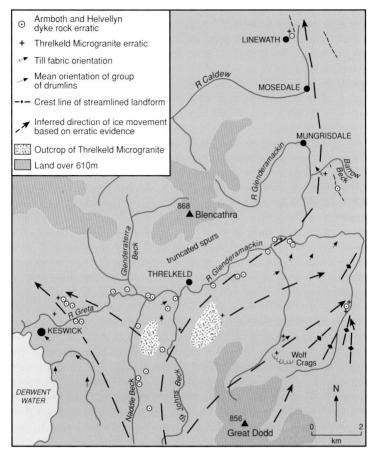

Figure 12: Direction of ice movement in the area north-east of Keswick

north-east along the Vale of Threlkeld, constrained by the massive bulk of Blencathra, before swinging to the north up what Hollingworth called 'the great through valley' which provides a low altitude route towards the Solway Plain. The valley is probably a remnant of a pre-glacial drainage system: it is now occupied by misfit streams. A low, indistinct watershed between Mungrisdale and the hamlet of Mosedale separates the south-flowing Glenderamackin drainage from that of the Caldew flowing to the north. The form and location of the valley is strongly influenced by geology. On the west, steep slopes are underlain by metamorphosed (hardened) Skiddaw Slates and the igneous complex of Carrock Fell. On the east, the Eycott Hills are composed of extrusive igneous rocks and carboniferous limestone outcrops around Hutton Roof (NY 373340). The present form of the valley is partly a result of glacial processes. The western valley side is a glacially over-steepened slope and dry meltwater channels can be seen on Souther Fell (NY 352286). On the floor of the valley are large streamlined landforms with glacial till

35

plastered around solid rock cores, e.g. Near Howe (NY 375288) and Bannest Hill (NY 358345).

Good exposures of till occur where the Mungrisdale road crosses Barrow Beck (NY 367291). To the east of the bridge, in a low river cliff, unweathered till outcrops. This is typical sub-glacial **lodgement till** of the last ice sheet to cross this area. It contains erratics from the south such as Threlkeld Microgranite and Armboth Quartz Porphyry from a dyke on the slopes to the west of Thirlmere. The orientation of the long axes of stones in the till indicates movement in a south-north direction. This exposure has been designated the **type site** of the Threlkeld Till, that is, the site where the local till of the last glaciation may be seen and where it displays its typical form. Exposures of the till high on the southern bank of the stream show a **gleyed soil** profile with extensive mottling in what is clearly a poorly drained parent material.

Five kilometres north of Barrow Beck, and through the hamlets of Mungrisdale and Mosedale, the road divides at Linewath (NY 352344) and a minor road leads north-west to a ford through Carrock Beck. In this area, landforms typical of ice stagnation during deglaciation can be seen.

To the east of the main road is a low ridge with an undulating crestline (Figure 13). Two exposures show that the ridge is composed of coarse, rounded gravels. The stone types include **granophyre** and gabbro from nearby Carrock Fell, metamorphosed slates from the Skiddaw massif and Threlkeld Microgranite and Armboth dyke rock from farther south. The presence of all these rock types implies transport from the south. The rounding of resistant igneous rocks, even those that have travelled less than 3km, suggests high-velocity water transport. To have reached this site much of the material must have been transported uphill, probably by both glacial and meltwater agencies, the latter operating sub-glacially under hydrostatic pressure. Modern glaciers are known to have extensive sub-glacial drainage systems – tunnels which may become choked with debris whenever water velocities are insufficient for transport of the load. Where this happens, depositional landforms (eskers) rather than erosional forms (meltwater channels) are produced. Many ridges of sands and gravels such as that at Linewath must be destroyed during deglaciation; for them to survive is the exception rather than the rule. However, under temperate conditions they are relatively stable because runoff, and therefore erosional processes, does not readily occur on such well drained surfaces. Frequent small pits in eskers, and in some areas extensive quarrying, indicate their value as a source of sand and gravel both for local farm use, for roads and foundations and for the building industry in general.

Looking westward from the crest of the esker, a series of flattish terrace surfaces can be identified (Figure 13). Some years ago, excellent exposures in the lowest of these surfaces, KT1, showed beds of coarse gravels alternating with sands, and a prominent silty-clay band separated an upper sequence from a lower one. Faults in the

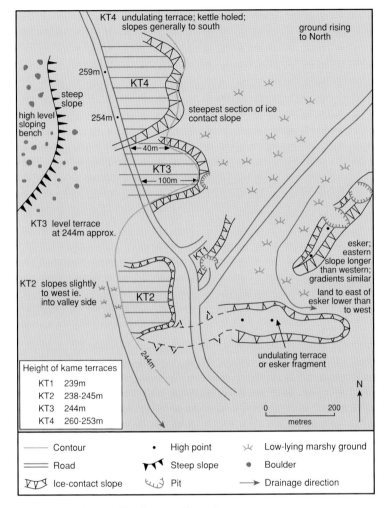

Figure 13: Field map of landforms at Linewath

beds were due either to the melting of buried ice or to the loss of support along the steep east-facing slope.

These terraces are interpreted as kame terraces, formed when coarse sediment accumulated between the valley side and a wasting body of ice occupying the valley bottom. During spring and summer, meltwater transported sands and gravels from both the ice surface and the valley side. During winter the area was occupied by shallow frozen pools and silts and clays settled out of suspension in the still water. If such an interpretation is correct the lowest, youngest terrace represents accumulation over a period of two summers and a winter. As the ice body in the valley bottom melted, successively lower terraces were formed and the steep, **ice-contact slope** was abandoned.

In some places, indicated by faulting of the sediments, this led to collapse.

The suite of landforms seen in this area – the esker, kame terraces and occasional kettle hole is typical of areas where ice has stagnated *in situ* – it ceased to move forward and melted away largely by the process of down wasting. Landforms such as eskers and kame terraces would not survive if the melting ice remained active. The reason why ice may cease to move during deglaciation may be little to do with sudden climatic change; often the explanation is that emerging topography has cut off a body of ice from its source; an isolated body of ice ceases to move and melts from the surface. Other areas of ice stagnation topography can be examined in Naddle, St John's in the Vale and, as already described, on the Keswick lowland.

The recognition that ice stagnation topography indicated a particular mode of deglaciation was an important step forward in the interpretation of many highland British landscapes. In the late 1950s J.B. Sissons introduced these ideas into Britain; with them came the equally important realisation that many meltwater channels and eskers represent sub-glacial drainage rather than drainage from the front or along the edge of ice.

At the foot of Carrock Fell, about a kilometre south of the kame terraces and on the western side of the road to Mungrisdale is a small quarry. The exposed sediments are clearly of local origin: they are predominantly angular blocks of granophyre from the steep slope to the west. This is a scree deposit produced by frost action at some time in the past. No additions to the scree are taking place at present; the surface is vegetated and a soil profile can be seen in the upper metre of the scree. It is probable that under periglacial conditions at the end of the last major glacial period and during the Loch Lomond Stadial screes such as this were actively accumulating. Incorporated into the angular scree deposit is the occasional glaciated boulder of gabbro or Borrowdale Volcanic type; these would have been left on the slopes during deglaciation and rolled to their present position as the scree accumulated. Many valley-side slopes in the Lake District are similarly covered by scree deposits which are now inactive and vegetated; this small quarry allows us a view of the base of a vegetated slope which would otherwise be hidden. Occasional exposures and experience in interpreting landforms suggest that the formation of scree under periglacial conditions was an important process in terms of contribution to the present form of the land surface.

Access

The sites described in this section can be visited on public footpaths or are on Common Land. The Keswick Lowland is farmed and part fenced. So it is important to remain on public footpaths which are clearly shown on the OS 1:25 000 Outdoor Leisure Map. Convenient parking for the Castlehead and Keswick Lowland sites is available in the Central and Lakeside car parks in Keswick and there is also a car park in Great Wood (NY 271213).

MOSEDALE BECK VALLEY

Dating glacial features is difficult. Dating landforms is particularly difficult because many of them are the product of several glaciations. Sediments offer slightly more hope of success in reconstructing landscape history, although over wide areas they tell a simple story – that of the most recent glaciation and its deglacial phase.

The valley of Mosedale Beck, south-east of Threlkeld (Figure 14) is unique in north-west England in that it provides evidence for three glacial events. In the base of the valley, at a number of sites between NY 35622413 and NY 35502332 is an olive-grey or very dark grey till severely weathered to a yellowish brown colour (Photo 8) – the Thornsgill Till (Figure 15). It overlies Skiddaw Slate bedrock and reaches a thickness of 14m at Caral Gully (NY 35562388). In its characteristic weathered condition it is a poorly-sorted bouldery till with little silt and clay and containing erratics from the west. The orientation of long axes of elongate pebbles also suggests ice movement from the west. Many stones in the till are soft and easily broken: they are partially or completely weathered and could not have been transported in this condition.

The weathering of stones, and the change of colour of the till, are aspects of soil development on a stable, vegetated land surface under

Photo 8: A severely weathered, rotted boulder in the pre-Devensian Thornsgill Till, Mosedale Beck valley Photo: John Boardman

humid conditions not unlike those of the present. The age of the till is unknown: organic sediments overlying it are beyond the range of radio-carbon dating (>50 000 years). The depth, up to 14m, and severity of weathering which occurred subsequent to its deposition, are quite unlike those of soils of the present interglacial. A long period of humid temperate conditions, perhaps several interglacials, may be inferred from the character of the weathering.

The survival of the Thornsgill Till through the Devensian, and perhaps earlier glacial stages, appears to be due to its location within

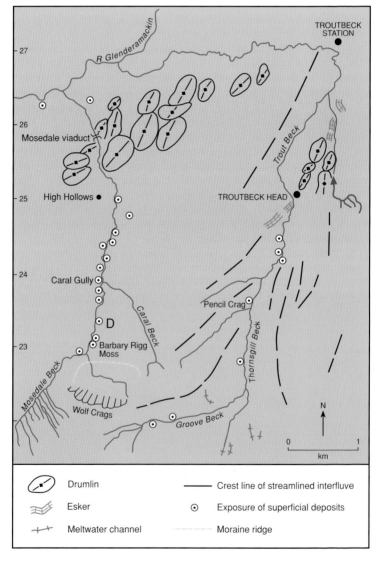

Figure 14: The Mosedale Beck valley

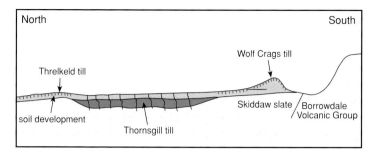

Figure 15: Profile of the Mosedale Beck valley to show the relationship between the three till units

a deep north-south trending valley cut in bedrock (Figure 15); this feature lies almost at right angles to the direction of ice movement across the area.

The relationship of the severely weathered Thornsgill Till to the Threlkeld Till of Devensian age may be examined at a river-cliff exposure on the east bank of Mosedale Beck (NY 355233; D on Figure 14). Here relatively unweathered Threlkeld Till overlies 2m of outwash gravels. Beneath the gravels is the Thornsgill Till, a series of black (manganese) stained beds of heavily weathered gravel and orange silty sands. The bedding appears to represent reworking of the till by periglacial processes after deposition. At the base of the section, and overlying Skiddaw Slate, is a thin unweathered till unit whose blue-grey colour vividly illustrates the effect of weathering on the Thornsgill Till.

Till of Devensian age is seen in many exposures high on the valley sides, which underlies much of the ground surface of the region. Below a zone of oxidation it is essentially unweathered; it contains hard, fresh stones and retains its original colour. The Threlkeld Till is the lodgement till of the most recent regional glaciation to affect northern England which culminated about 18 000 years ago. Erratics, streamlined landforms such as the drumlins north of High Hollows (Figure 14), and stone orientations, imply ice movement from the west and south-west, that is, the high ground of the central Lake District (Figure 12). The wide valley which runs eastwards from Threlkeld is a continuation of the Thirlmere trough to the south and was evidently a major route for last glaciation ice, as it had been for the ice which deposited the Thornsgill Till. The final glacial event to affect the area was of a more limited character.

At the head of Mosedale is Wolf Crags corrie (Photo 9). Given that its north-facing aspect would have protected accumulating snow from the sun, it is unusually low in altitude. Another factor in its development is the extensive area of high ground to the south from which snow would have blown into the corrie. The corrie backwall is cut in resistant lavas and ashes of the Borrowdale Volcanic Group: the important geological boundary of these rocks and the older Skiddaw Group runs through the Wolf Crags corrie basin. Around the corrie is an impressive moraine ridge, Barbary Rigg on the OS map, built by the small corrie glacier that occupied this site during the Loch Lomond Stadial. This was one of 64 glaciers in the Lake District at that time which are more fully discussed in the section on Blea Water Corrie.

Within the Mosedale valley are also found river terraces. These are indicative of episodes of stream incision and aggradation and are composed of coarse gravels and sand derived from the till. The size of many of the boulders in the terraces suggests high velocity flow during floods, but the age of these events is difficult to establish.

It is likely that incision began as the Late Devensian ice sheet wasted and continued during the Loch Lomond Stadial when meltwater from ice at Wolf Crags and snow in the upper basin would have led to annual floods of high magnitude. These would be especially effective because of the presence of frozen ground and the absence of vegetation. The higher terraces in Mosedale, those over about 4m above the present channel, show well developed podzols, gleys and brown earth soils, their inception probably dating from Late Devensian and early Flandrian time. Below about 4m there is evidence for comparatively recent flood events. The soils are thin and poorly developed in unweathered gravels. Large boulders are concentrated in bars such as the one 160m south-east of the derelict High Hollows Farm. Dry, braided channels and boulder strewn terraces occur up to 4m above the channel, e.g. at NY 356242 and NY

Photo 9: The moraine ridge and Wolf Crags corrie seen from the north
Photo: John Boardman

356245 (Photo 10). Many of these features may be the result of a cloudburst over Mosedale in 1749 for which there is documentary evidence. Such occasional floods during the Flandrian emphasise that intermittent landscape change in deforested, high-gradient upland catchments is still possible although the major landforms of the area are inherited from periods of glacial and periglacial conditions.

Photo 10: River terraces and boulder bars in the Mosedale Beck valley
Photo: John Boardman

Access

There is no public footpath along the Mosedale Beck valley. The western valley side and the beck are on Common Land but parts of the eastern side beyond the wall/fence are owned by Mr Titterington, High Gate Close Farm, from whom permission to visit that area should be obtained (Tel: 017687 79293).

Access to the Mosedale Beck valley is best obtained along the Old Coach Road from High Row to the Barbary Rigg moraine. Vehicles can be parked at High Row (NY 380220). It is a 30 minute walk to the moraine.

PATTERNED GROUND ON GRASMOOR

Patterned ground, of the type generally associated with periglacial conditions, can be seen on high flat summits of the Lake District such as those on Grasmoor (Photo 11), Helvellyn and Skiddaw. The most common form of patterned ground is the sorted stripe. These lines of stone are formed under contemporary climatic conditions of high rainfall and mean winter temperatures of between 4°C and −3°C. Three to six times each winter, short periods of intense cold occur; these last several days, during which the ground may freeze to a depth of 30cm.

Photo 11: Sorted stripes on the summit of Grasmoor (pencil for scale)
Photo: John Boardman

Dr T.N. Caine has described sorted stripe sites to the east of the summit of Grasmoor, on Sand Hill (NY 187219), and to the north on Hopegill Head (NY 186222). Details of other sites are provided by Warburton (1985). Sites in the Grasmoor area are on Skiddaw Slate bedrock which is very susceptible to frost shattering. The material in which the stripes are developed is predominantly gravel-size with a little sand and less than 7% silt and clay.

Two groups of sorted stripes are to be found on the summit of Grasmoor: these are to the north of the highest point around NY 175205 and to the east around NY 184206. Typically stripes are found on slopes of 6 to 20°; they are vegetation free, low-angle screes. The stones in the fine stripes are usually less than 2cm and those in the coarse stripes are 7-15cm in length. The coarse stripes are orientated directly down the maximum slope and long axes of stones have a similar preferred orientation. Marked surface stones have been shown to move 5 to 20cm downslope during the winter, but stones at 10cm depth record little movement. Widths vary but the fine stripes are

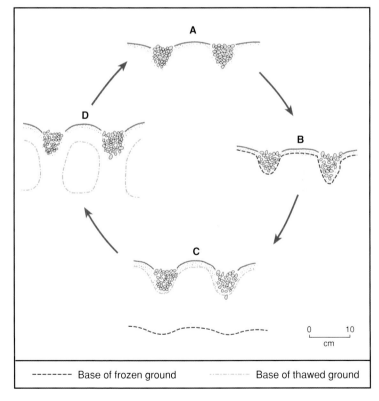

Figure 16: Freeze and thaw in sorted stripes
(a) completely thawed; (b) freezing extends downwards faster under coarse stripes than under fine; (c) thawing occurs faster under coarse stripes than under fine, drainage takes place through the coarse stripes; (d) frozen areas remain only under fine ridges
From Caine, 1963; reproduced by permission of Geografiska Annaler

generally between 8 and 45cm and the coarse between 5 and 10cm.

The maintenance of sorted patterned ground is due to the heaving of the fine stripes with their greater moisture content (Figure 16). Because there is slow movement downslope the heaving tends to concentrate the large particles since these slide into the coarse stripes.

What is not fully understood is how the sorting is initiated. One likely explanation is that there were particle-size variations in the original scree material which have become accentuated by freeze-thaw processes; other explanations include the overturning of the soil due to convective currents.

It is worth noting the small dimensions of this contemporary patterned ground. Stripes of much larger dimensions (e.g. 1m across) have been recorded in North Wales: these are inactive, fossil features apparently formed under more extreme periglacial conditions, probably in association with permafrost.

The contemporary origin of small-scale patterned ground can be demonstrated: it is found on recent mining waste in the northern Lake District, and when disturbed can reform in the course of a few years. The high-level sites on Grasmoor vary from year to year, the clarity of the patterning apparently depending on winter climatic conditions.

Access and safety

Recommended routes onto the high summit plateau of Grasmoor are from Buttermere via Whiteless Pike or from Stair, in Newlands, via Causey Pike and Crag Hill. These routes are for the experienced mountain walker. It is dangerous to take parties onto Grasmoor in mist as there are precipitous slopes near to the patterned ground sites.

CORRIES OF THE NORTHERN LAKE DISTRICT

Dr Ian Evans has identified 158 corries in the English Lake District, 28 of which are on Skiddaw Group rocks. Of these, the ten corries in the northern fells of Skiddaw and Blencathra form a distinct group (Figure 17). This upland acted as a local ice source; ice from the south (or north) does not appear to have overrun the area (Figure 12). Except for the corries, the landscape has been fashioned largely by periglacial rather than glacial processes.

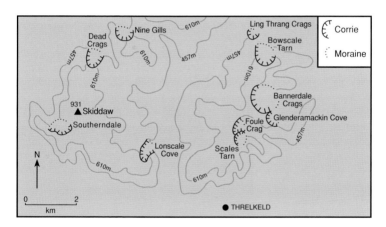

Figure 17: Cirques of the northern Lake District

Using a morphological grading scheme the corries are described as: classic; well defined; definite; poor; marginal. Of the ten northern corries, those at Bowscale Tarn and Scales Tarn are of classic form. Six of the corries, including Bowscale and Bannerdale, are developed in Skiddaw Slates that have been thermally metamorphosed by the Skiddaw Granite intrusion which produced a harder, more resistant rock. In general, the corries face north-east and were thus protected from solar radiation. Their easterly and northerly position in relation to high land also means that south to south-westerly winds would blow drifting snow into the corries adding to their effectiveness as snow-gathering sites; as they enlarged they would become more effective – a good example of positive feedback in the development of landforms.

47

Bowscale Tarn Corrie

This is a relatively accessible corrie reached by a track and path from the village of Bowscale (NY 358317). The track ascends the southern slopes of the Caldew valley – a small glacial trough. Old river channels are visible on the floodplain below. From the track the poorly developed ('marginal') corrie at Ling Thrang Crags can be seen. It is at a low altitude (315m) for corrie development. Just before reaching Tarn Sike, the stream draining Bowscale Tarn, the path crosses an area of debris flow that covers the hillside from the corrie moraine to the floodplain of the Caldew. These were presumably the result of glacial meltwater mobilizing glacial debris on the moraine and hillside below.

Bowscale Corrie is an impressive landform with steep north and east-facing headwalls, a tarn with maximum depth of 16.5m, and a surprisingly large moraine ridge now breached by Tarn Sike. Evans' reconstruction of the last (Loch Lomond Stadial) glacier to occupy the corrie gives dimensions of 450 x 430m with a maximum depth of 95m and ice velocities of 35m per year. The moraine could be about 30m thick with a volume of 680 000m³, representing erosion from the headwall and basin of 5-10m.

Based on analysis of plant pollen in mud at the base of the tarn, Pennington (1988) showed that the corrie was occupied by ice in the early part of the Loch Lomond Stadial. However, it is difficult to envisage such an impressive moraine being wholly the result of erosional processes during a period of a few hundred years. Alternatively, it is also likely to be the result of ice occupancy and erosional processes in the Dimlington Stadial. The size of the moraine is, therefore, not very useful in terms of estimating rates of glacial erosion over a known time period since we are not sure as to the time

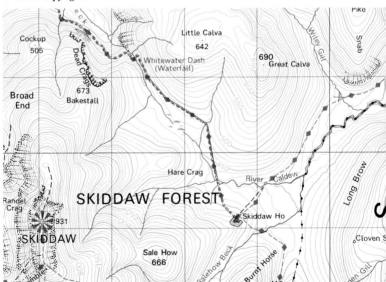

period involved. The corrie form (as opposed to the moraine) certainly developed over many glacial episodes during the Quaternary.

Bannerdale Corrie

The corrie at the head of the Bannerdale Beck valley can be reached from Bowscale Tarn by ascending the steep grassy eastern wall of the corrie and heading south-west to the summit of Bowscale Fell (NY 333306). The cliffs forming the east-facing headwall of Bannerdale Corrie begin about 400m south of the summit.

Bannerdale is a 'well defined' corrie with a boggy floor rather than a tarn. The steepest and largest part of the headwall faces northeast and therefore the corrie is asymmetric. The central section of a long, low moraine ridge has been removed by meltwater. Bannerdale differs from Bowscale Corrie in that it is situated at the head of a short valley. It was presumably the source for a valley glacier under conditions which favoured glaciation; at other times, such as the Loch Lomond Stadial, it was occupied by a small corrie glacier whose extent is indicated by the moraine ridge.

Access

The walk described is one for good, clear weather although the track and path to Bowscale Tarn is safe in poor weather. From Bannerdale Crags there is an easy descent to the village of Mungrisdale or one can head south, skirting Scales Tarn corrie to reach the summit of Blencathra from which there are numerous routes of descent. This is a good-weather walk for experienced and fit walkers.

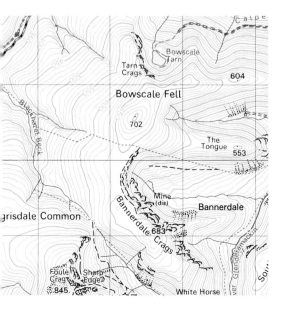

GLOSSARY

Andesite Fine-grained intermediate volcanic igneous rock containing the feldspars oligoclase or andesine.

BP Date in years before the present.

Basalt Fine-grained basic igneous rock.

Batholith Large intrusive mass of igneous rock usually of granitic type.

Brown earth Acid, well-drained soil with uniformly brownish coloured profile.

Dimlington Stadial Cold period during Devensian Stage between 26 000 and 13 000 BP when last regional glaciation of northern Britain occurred.

Dolerite Medium-grained basic igneous rock frequently occurring as dykes, sills or volcanic necks.

Gley soils Soils of poorly drained sites characteristically with grey colours and yellowish mottles as a result of waterlogging.

Granophyre Medium-grained acid igneous rock of similar composition to granite with intergrowths of quartz and feldspar crystals.

Ice-contact slope A slope, e.g. on a kame terrace, which was formerly supported by ice; the slope may collapse after the ice melts.

Little Ice Age Cold period between 1550 and 1700 AD when mean annual temperatures in England were about 1°C lower than those for 1920-60.

Loch Lomond Stadial Cold period 11 000 to 10 000 BP with restricted glaciation in British uplands, i.e. Loch Lomond Advance. Summer temperatures were about 10°C lower than those of the present time in England.

Lodgement Till Till (see below) deposited under moving ice when individual rock particles or debris aggregates are 'lodged' against bedrock as a result of frictional drag and localised ice melt.

Permafrost Ground layer that remains below 0°C for a number of years. Above permafrost is the active layer which thaws each summer.

Podzol A soil with a dark-coloured B horizon enriched in iron, aluminium and humus often underlying a pale-coloured E horizon.

Pyroclastic rocks Rocks consisting of fragments of volcanic material blown into the atmosphere by explosive activity.

Talus A sloping heap of rock debris (scree) at the foot of a mountain slope.

Till A sediment deposited from glacial ice which is usually poorly sorted and contains erratics.

Type site A reference section where a particular geological unit is well displayed, accessible and shows typical attributes.

BIBLIOGRAPHY

Boardman, J. (ed) (1981) *Field Guide to Eastern Cumbria*. Quaternary Research Association, Cambridge.

Boardman, J. (1982) 'Glacial geomorphology of the Keswick area, northern Cumbria' in *Proceedings, Cumberland Geological Society*, 4, 115-34.

Boardman, J. (ed) (1985) *Field Guide to the Periglacial Landforms of Northern England*. Quaternary Research Association, Cambridge.

Boardman, J. and Walden, J. (eds) (1994) *Cumbria Field Guide*. Quaternary Research Association, Oxford.

Briggs, D. (1977) *Sediments*. Butterworth.

Caine, T.N. (1963) 'The origin of sorted stripes in the Lake District, Northern England' in *Geografiska Annaler*, 45A, 172-9.

Clough, R.McK. (1977) 'Some aspects of corrie initiation and evolution in the English Lake District' in *Proceedings Cumberland Geological Society*, 3, 209-32.

Evans, I.S. and Cox, N.J. (1995) 'The form of glacial cirques in the English Lake District, Cumbria' in *Zeitschrift fur Geomorphologie*, 39, 2, 175-202.

King, C.A.M. (1976) *The Geomorphology of the British Isles: Northern England*. Methuen.

Lewis, W.V. (ed) (1960) *Investigations on Norwegian Cirque Glaciers*. Royal Geographical Society, London.

Marr, J.E. (1916) *The Geology of the Lake District*. Cambridge University Press.

Moseley, F. (ed) (1978) *The Geology of the Lake District*. Yorkshire Geological Society.

Newson, M.D. and Leeks, G.J. (1985) 'Mountain bedload yields in the United Kingdom from undisturbed fluvial environments' in *Earth Surface Processes and Landforms*, 10, 413-16.

Pearsall, W.H. and Pennington, W. (1973) *The Lake District*. Collins.

Pennington, W. (1978) 'Quaternary geology' in Moseley, F. (ed) *The Geology of the Lake District*, Yorkshire Geological Society, 207-25.

Shackleton, E.H. (1975) *Lakeland Geology Where to Go: What to See* (third edition). Dalesman.

Shackleton, E.H. (1975) *Geological Excursions in Lakeland*. Dalesman.

Sissons, J.B. (1980) 'The Loch Lomond Advance in the Lake District, northern England' in *Transactions Royal Society Edinburgh*, Earth Sciences, 71, 13-27.

Warburton, J. (1985) 'Contemporary patterned ground (sorted stripes) in the Lake District' in Boardman, J. (ed) *Field Guide to the Periglacial Landforms of Northern England*. Quaternary Research Association, Cambridge.